CHARLES DICKENS

JOE MATTHEWS

DAVE McCLUSKEY

©2016 by Joe Matthews, Dave McCluskey and the respective creators.
Published by Impact Printworks.
Hillcot, Hiraddug Road, Dyserth, LL18 6HS
impactprintworks@live.co.uk
Joe Matthews and Dave McCluskey have asserted their rights under the
Copyright Designs and Patents Act 1988 to be identified as the authors of this work.
All rights reserved. No part of this book may be reproduced, stored in a retrieval system or
transmitted in any form without the prior permission of the publisher or copyright holder.
Print edition ISBN 978-0-9934490-2-4
Printing in UK

Special thanks to Jo Whitehead, Colin Meredith, James Hill, John Matthews & Jarrar Haider.

A CHRISTMAS CAROL

story by
CHARLES DICKENS

artwork & script by
JOE MATTHEWS

verse by
DAVE McCLUSKEY

DEDICATIONS

To the memory of Richard Matthews, I know you'd have loved to read this
book on Christmas Eve with a glass or two.
To Dad & Mam, thanks for making our Christmasses so special.
To Michelle, special thanks for tolerating me spending months listening to
Christmas tunes while making this book!
To Chris, Jamie & Archie, love you loads.
Joe Matthews 2016

To the memory of Ted McCluskey (Dad), Ebenezer past and present...
To Ann McCluskey (Mum), because I know I'm the most special...
To my sisters Annmarie and Helen who have supported me and helped me every step of the way.
To Grace McCluskey, my constant inspiration.
Brother-in-laws, nieces, nephews, friends, hangers on, distant colleagues... the list is endless...
God Bless Us... Every One
Dave McCluskey 2016

Looking hard at the figure
He let out a small moan
"If you're a Spirit that was foretold?"
"I'd rather be left alone"

"I am here to aid in your salvation"
The figure it did squeak
Scrooge was shocked, taken aback
His face it looked so bleak

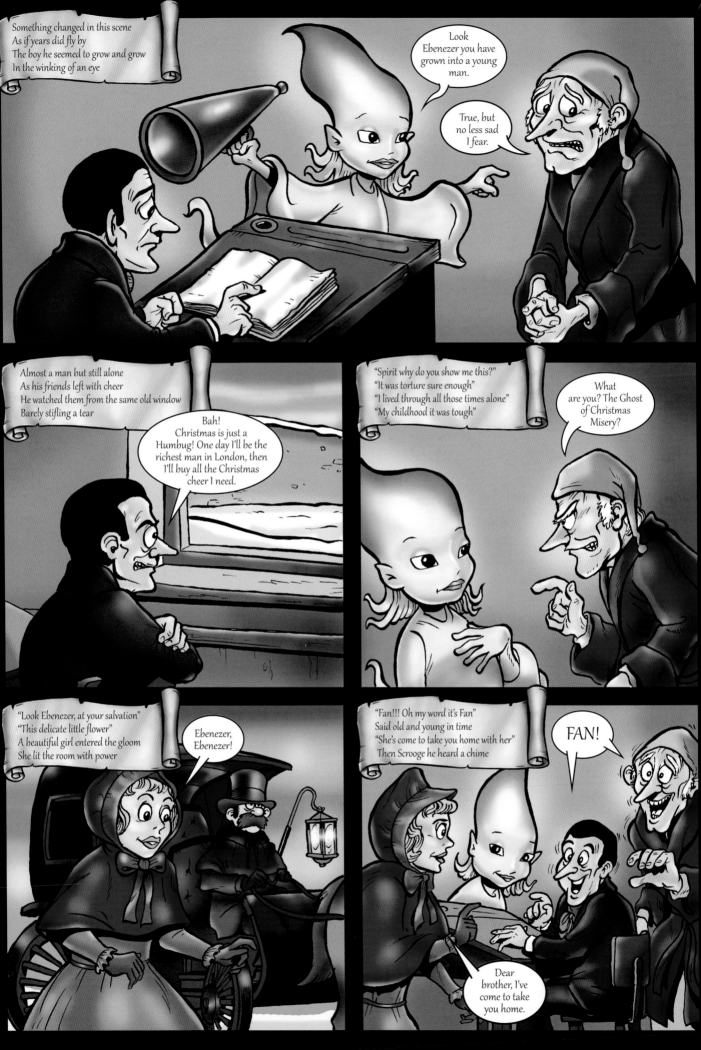

21

23

His robe it was the finest green
His beard thick and lush
With massive hands behind Scrooge's back
Gave him a little push

Who paid for all this food?

Ho, Ho, Ho!

Now this scene it was unique
Although it was his room
It had never seen such festive cheer
It was usually in gloom

'tis everymans.

Well he won't mind me helping myself to this pie.

Ho, Ho, Ho!

"I bet that you've never witnessed"
"The likes of me before."
"But I have many brothers Scrooge."
"Eighteen hundred so, or more."

"Eighteen hundred brothers"
"I would hate to see your bills"
The roar of laughter that boomed out
Was enough to give you chills

I hope they're not all as loud as you?

"I'm the Spirit of Christmas Present"
"I go where there is cheer"
"I am goodwill to men worldwide"
"Now, and throughout the year

Spirit. Take me where you will. I went forth last night and I learnt a lesson. If you have anything to teach me, let me profit by it.

Can I take a doggie bag?

I'll shrink down to your size. It'll be easier for the cartoonist.

"We're going on a journey Scrooge"
"We'll travel far and wide"
"But I'm still in my nightclothes now"
"I cannot go outside"

"Forgive me Spirit, but I seem to see,"
"A little something, like a claw"
As the Spirit pulled back his coat
Scrooge balked at what he saw

It's...
some kind of
claw!

Two thin and dirty children
Were lurking underneath
As they were exposed to the light
They hissed and bared their teeth

RRRRAGH!

Watch
it! They're a bit
nasty these
two!

RRRRAGH!

Yikes!

RRRRAGH!

Claw like hands ripped at Scrooge
As they tried to grab him close
Their evil, dirty desperate faces
Made Ebenezer feel morose

Are
there no
PRISONS?

Are
there no
WORKHOUSES?

"Spirit, these wretched beings."
"Tell me are they yours?"
The Ghost of Christmas Present looked
At the children on all fours

"Ignorance and Want are these"
"Mankind's own offsprings"
"Beware them both old Ebenezer"
"But most what Ignorance brings"

I'm sorry
Spirit. Truly
I am!

The Ghost of Christmas Present left
As the mood did shift again
A spinning spiral enraptured him
It played with his poor brain

Spirit.
I'm sorry. Don't
leave me.

The light then faded all around
With a tolling of a bell
Ebenezer looked about him scared
Was this his own death knell?

BONG! BONG! BONG! BONG!

He stood there out in the snow
Alone, scared and cold
With dread he awaited the appearance of
The last Spirit foretold

Brrrrr!
It... it... it's f, f, f, flippin'
f, f, f, freezin'

A gloom set deep within his heart
He fell down to his knees
An icy sharpness pierced his soul
As horror, in him did squeeze

CAW!
CAW!

He opened one petrified eye
Dreading what it would see
A black feathered raven from above
Descended from a tree

CAW! CAW!
CAW!

Yeahh!!

The raven looked at Ebenezer
A harbinger of doom
It's dark red eyes they glared at him
As if from beyond the tomb

It grew and grew into a shape
A figure in a hood
A long black gown from head to toe
Enough to freeze your blood

It had no face, this dark Spirit
Just a gaping, looming hole
It's skeletal hand pointed at Scrooge
As the midnight bell did toll

BONG!

BONG!

BONG!

BONG!

BONG!

"Are you the Spirit of Christmas?"
"Of the ones yet to come?"
"Of all the Spirits, I fear you most."
"To your will I must succumb."

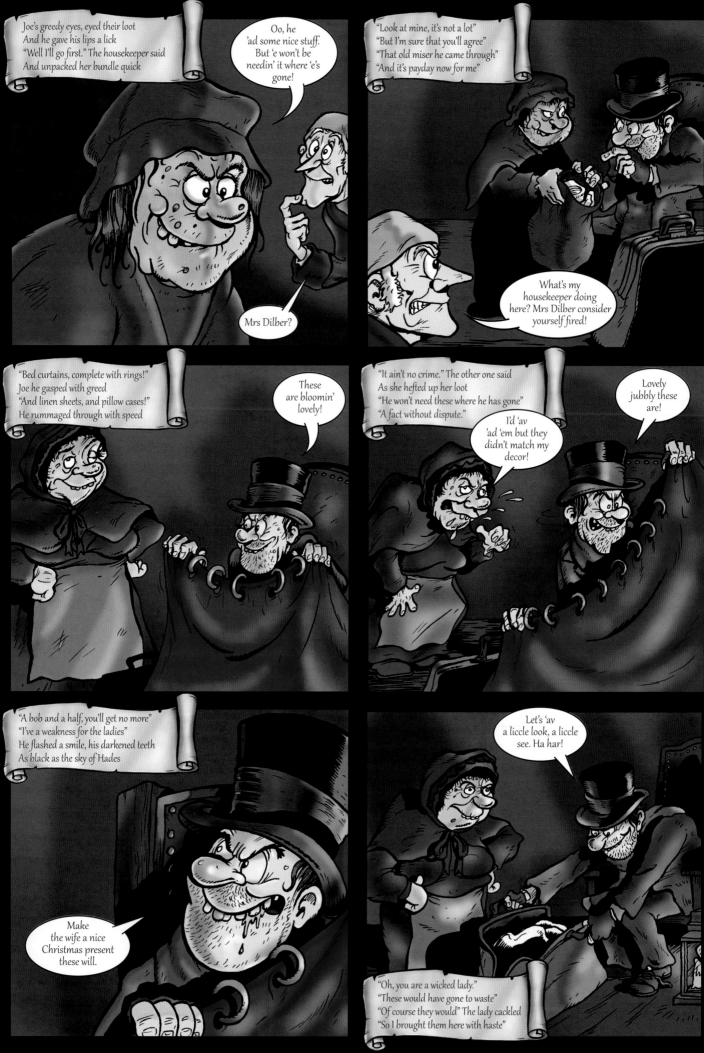

42

44

47

The ground beneath him fell away
Into to a vast abyss
The red and fiery glow below him
Gave out an awful hiss

Spirit! Hear me!

As Ebenezer descended down
Into this hellish place
The Ghost of Christmas Yet To Come
Revealed to him his face

I AM NOT THE MAN I WAS!

It was Ebenezer's very own
His likeness stared him down
A mean and stony chiselled face
With a permanent ugly frown

GOOD SPIRIT!

I WILL CHANGE!

Down and down and down he fell
Into the hellish pit
The infernal inferno below it beckoned
Flames they hissed and spit

"Now listen buck, is the turkey there?"
"The prize one on the sill?"
"The one as big as me you mean?"
"Why yes it is there still"

The big whopper?

Ebenezer gave a snort
"Oh what a clever boy"
"Go over there and buy it lad"
"I'm about to spread some joy"

This boy is a nutter. Ha!

"Cor, yeah mate, pull the other one"
"Coz that has bells that ring"
The boy was about to run away
When Scrooge said one last thing

Look! Jingle Bells!

Did someone mention the butchers?

"Bring the butcher back with you"
"I'll pay you half a shilling"
The boy he looked at Scrooge amazed
Then ran off, more than willing

YOWZER!

Sausages! Sausages, Sausages!

"I'll send it to Bob Cratchit's house"
"He won't know who it's from"
Just then a knock came on his door
Scrooge answered with aplomb

It'll be better than that poor excuse for a goose, I'm sure!

Morning. Mrs Dilber.

The old woman standing there
Was holding out a tray
On it was a steaming kettle
Her hair was long and grey

Eh? Oh 'er, mornin' Mr. Scrooge.

"Do you know old Camden Town?"
"I know it's far away"
"Well get a cab to this address."
"I need this there today."

Ha, ha, ha! You're like a double act.

Wotcher! Ya' nearly squashed me flat!

The butcher looked at the address
And the money he'd been handed
He sped off so fast right then
The boy felt that he'd been stranded

Make haste my dear fellow.

Scrooge held out his hand to him
"Take this boy, you 'av earned"
The boys' eyes wide, looked at him
"It's for the lessons I 'av learned"

Now you go and treat your dear old Mother and Father.

Wow!

Slurp! Sausages!

"Corr, thank you Mister and no mistake"
The boy called as he ran
Counting the fortune in his hands
He now had a Christmas plan

No fear. It's off to 'Ye olde Sweet Shoppe'

And some Sausages!

Scrooge laughed and walked away
Into the busy square
Towards a crowd around the good deed men
Who'd set their stall up there

Merry Christmas to you both.

Merry Christmas Mr Scrooge.

They were handing out hot food
To the hungry and the needy
The first thing that Ebenezer noticed
Not one of them were greedy

Fank you guv'

An orderly queue had formed around
Gratitude on their faces
Receiving their small bundles of food
With dignity and graces

Scrooge he walked right up to them
Both their faces fell
"Oh Mister Scrooge please do forgive"
"But we're busy can't you tell?"

Huh, the cheek of it. Back of the...

...queue Mr Scrooge!

"Oh I can see you're busy"
"And I can see all your good work"
"Please allow me to help you here"
"This I don't want to shirk"

Hmmm. About yesterday!

He whispered into one man's ear
"Do you think that's quite enough?"
The man he looked at Scrooge amazed
But he knew it was no bluff

Bless...

...my soul!

"Why haven't I done this before?"
"This sliding on the ice"
"I've never felt so much alive"
"It really does feel nice"

Yahoo! Merry Christmas, Everyone!

He talked to the street vendors
Who all seemed to respond
They wished him Merry Christmas
He'd made a special bond

Merry Christmas Sir.

HOT PIES

Got any Sausages?

The day it seemed so wonderful
It was like a whole new world
A different level opened up to him
His head it whirled and whirled

What a glorious feeling Christmas is.

There was happiness and joy abound
Greeting all with smiles
The people they all seemed so happy
Regardless of their trials

"So this must be the Christmas spirit"
He marvelled in his mind
"All this time I've denied myself"
"Being mean and so unkind"

I'll keep this feeling all year round.

A thought occurred, one quite strange
Filled with wonder and with dread
It was something that he'd long neglected
His own Nephew Fred

Munch. Munch. Munch. Munch!

He walked along the street outside
He could hear the sounds of fun
It was so cold out there in the street
Inside Christmas had begun

He went and knocked on the door
He was answered by the maid
"How can I help you today?"
She asked as music played

A merry Christmas to you my dear.

59

"Is the master of the house about?"
She flashed a great big smile
"Oh yes the master's home alright"
"They've been in there a while"

I'm his Uncle. I've been invited.

"Allow me to show you the way"
"Oh that wont be required"
"I know the way into the room"
Scrooge was then inspired

I was here later. Er' I mean I've been before.

He crept up to the door ahead
And listened for a while
Fun and laugher did abound
Causing him to smile

Fred!

He popped his head around the door
The music it stopped still
Everyone looked, their jaws all dropped
At who was standing in the sill

Bless my soul. Uncle Ebenezer!

"Uncle Ebenezer?"
Came Fred's excited shout
"I am so glad that you've turned up."
"To end your Christmas drought"

Come in. Come in Uncle and join our party!

"I wasn't so sure you'd have me here"
"Due to the awful things I've said"
"Christmas is a time for forgiveness Uncle"
Scrooge's face blushed red

Don't mention it dear Uncle.

"And you my beautiful, beautiful Niece"
"Can you forgive me too?"
"A stupid old and pompous fool"
"Twisted through and through"

It's a pleasure to have you Uncle.

"Oh Uncle Scrooge you have made the day"
"I see it on Fred's face"
"You've brought happiness to our gathering"
"With presence and with grace"

I'm so happy I could pop!

"Topper start the music"
"I think we'll dance a waltz"
"Well hold onto your hats." Topper shouted
"I'll play it without faults"

Let's get this party started Topper!

Ebenezer turned to his Nephew's wife
His hand out in a stretch
"Will you make an old fool happy?"
"And please forgive this wretch"

Let's dance dear Uncle.

To the sound he's playing on the piano!

They danced and sang the live long day
They ate and made so merry
Topper proposed to his dearly beloved
Who blushed red as a cherry

Yahoo! Merry Christmas, Everyone!

Ebenezer, happier than he'd been in years
As the day drew to an end
He saw the room was filled with love
For his Nephew and his friend

"Fred I'm sorry, I let you down."
"Your Mother made me swear"
"An oath to see to your every need"
"But I feel I've not been fair"

Your Mother would have been very proud of you Fred, as am I.

Thank you Uncle. That means a lot to me.

"I was set against your marriage"
"I see now all my folly"
"This marriage has made you the man I see"
"Today amidst the holly"

Over here old boy!

No. This way!

"I could not be a prouder man"
"If I lived a hundred years"
"The love I've felt in here today"
"Has brought me close to tears"

Wonderful party. Wonderful games. Won-der-ful happiness!

"My door it's always open Uncle"
"You're welcome day or night"
As Scrooge bade all of his farewells
He knew he'd be alright

We will do this again soon. I promise.

That Christmas night as he walked home
His eyes they roamed the sky
He was searching for his brother Marley
With a smile that was so wry

The
stars look
very different
today!

"Thank you Jacob for your help"
"To see the error of my ways"
"I'll keep this Christmas spirit with me"
"Right through all my days"

A
shooting star. I'll make
a wish for you Jacob
Marley.

Jacob
my old friend, I hope
you find peace and you're
free from the burden
you carry.

Whoop,
whoop! I'm
free!

He heard a strange old rattling noise
An odd feeling he had owned
A weight it lifted from his shoulders
For sins he had atoned

In joyous spirits he reached his door
And stared hard at the knocker
"Ha ha, it was you who started this"
"My day has been a shocker"

He gave the knocker a jaunty tap
And stepped into his house
Tonight there was nothing stirring
Not even a small mouse

I shall
love this knocker
always.

Scrooge he sighed as he stepped inside
This day? How could he match it?
Then a thought occurred that caused a smile
A thought of old Bob Cratchit

I can't
wait to see Bob
Cratchit's face.

Scrooge reached work the next day
In the office he was alone
He watched the clock tick to 9:05
When he heard the front door moan

Ho, ho, ho!
He's late. I knew he
would be.

In crept a timid Bob Cratchit
Who spared him half a glance
Towards his boss sat at his desk
He thought he'd take a chance

Quietly
does it!

He quickly opened his ledger
Then he began to write
He felt a gaze burning down
It made him feel contrite

"Mr Cratchit, a moment please."
The stern voice filtered in
Bob he stood with his head down
His face filled with chagrin

CRATCHIT!

OH OH!

"What time do you call this man?"
Scrooge was full of scorn
"I'm sorry Sir it won't happen again"
"I made rather merry yesterday morn"

Morning!

AFTERNOON!

CRATCHIT!

Scrooge he stood to his full height
He took in a large breath
His face was stern and filled with anger
To Bob he looked like death

64

Bob's eyes were closed and ready
For the scolding he would get
"Cratchit our hours of operation are..."
"From nine 'til seven, set"

I was making rather merry yesterday!

"I am so sorry, I will work late"
"To work up what I owe"
Scrooge's heart could not withstand
Bob's sorrow and his woe

And. It is only once a year Mr Scrooge!

"Robert Cratchit, because you're late"
"I'll not let this continue"
He tried his best to hide a smile
He stretched his neck bone sinew

"I really have no other recourse"
"This will not go away"
Bob sealed himself for the bad news
"So I'll have to raise your pay!"

Eh?

Bob's face recoiled as if slapped
But then he opened one small eye
Realisation of what Scrooge had said
His throat, it went bone dry

Who are you and what have you done to the real Mr Scrooge?

Scrooge's face it beamed at him
The smile made him look moony
Bob looked around for some sort of weapon
To fend off this raving loony

He's finally flipped. He's lost his marbles!

And Tiny Tim, who didn't die
Became Scrooge's new found son
The little lad he smiled and said...
God bless Us, Every One!
God bless Us, Every One!
You said it lad.
The End

A CHRISTMAS CAROL GALLERY

It gives me great pleasure to invite fellow cartoonists and family to contribute their character sketches from A Christmas Carol to my version of the book. It is an honour to present them to you here.
May they haunt your house pleasantly.

Joe Matthews 2016

CHRIS MATTHEWS

My son, Chris Matthews, has watched me draw cartoons all his life. At the age of 6 he created his own comic character 'Brainy Knot'. I'm proud to have influenced his avid reading, book collecting and appreciation of comic art.

NIGEL PARKINSON

Nigel Parkinson is an extremely gifted cartoonist. He draws 'Dennis the Menace' and 'The Bash Street Kids' in The Beano.
One of my dreams when I was a kid was to draw for The Beano, and thankfully something I achieved with 'Ivy The Terrible'
and 'Ball Boy' in 1987.

JOHN MATTHEWS

As kids, my brother John and I would spend hours drawing our favourite superheroes and cartoons. Happy days indeed. Although John hasn't drawn for many years, I love his version of Marley's Ghost.

PHIL ELLIOTT

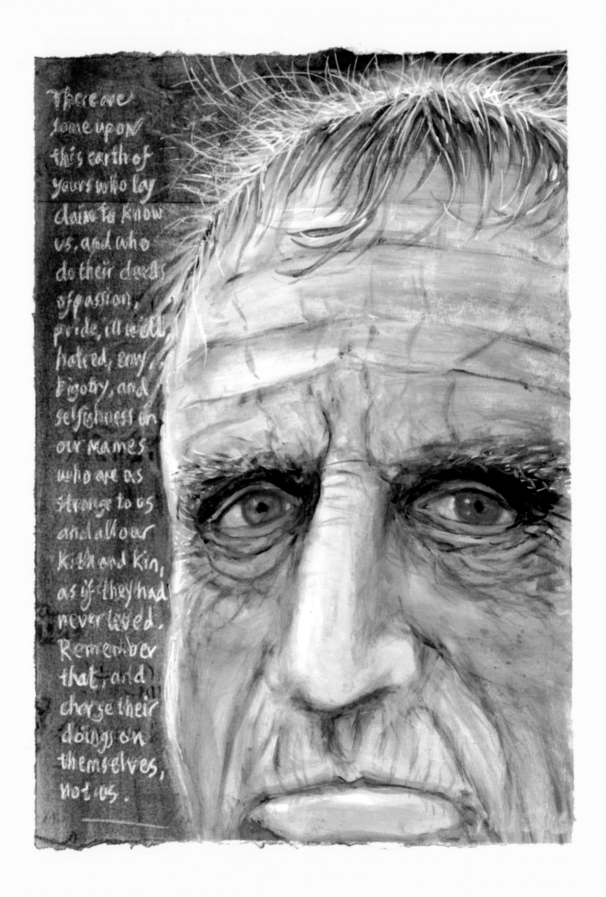

Phil Elliott has been working in comics since the mid 1970's when we contributed to each others' magazines as young teenagers. Phil is an extremely talented artist who's work has appeared in Aces Weekly, Real Ghostbusters along with doing the colour work for Dr Who comics and Torchwood for IDW Publishing.

RON TINER

Ron Tiner is such a well respected and brilliant illustrator. He used to teach narrative sequential illustration with
scenes from this Dickens classic, and he complimented my artwork for "such a lot of the aspects of good storytelling"
he wanted his students to get across. I'm so proud to have one of his sketches in my book.

HUNT EMERSON

Mr. & Mrs. Fezziwig

Hunt Emerson has been a favourite cartoonist of mine simply forever. I suggested to Hunt that he should do a cartoon version of A Christmas Carol, but when he saw some of my early character sketches he inspired the confidence in me, to do it myself.

John Charles

Charles at Stoke-Con 2014, the first comic con that I attended as a trader. He was the first person
...nsters Comic. John teaches comic art at the University of Stoke. The students are a lucky bunch...

CREATING A PANEL FOR A CHRISTMAS CAROL

This was a pivitol moment in the story. It needed to emphasise the close bond between Bob Cratchit and his youngest son Tiny Tim.
There is an obvious difference between Bob the family man, and Bob Scrooge's clerk. Family is everything to Bob. My original sketch for this panel (in blue pencil as I always do) had Bob and Tiny Tim trundling through the deserted streets of London town.

At the inking stage, I lost the building. Not because I was too lazy to ink them in, but because I wanted to focus on this being their special time together. Walking home, singing and happy. A real father and son moment.

I then scanned the inked page in and started to add flat colours to the image. I started this with a bright blue sky but then realised that Bob would have worked until 7pm on Christmas Eve. A winters night would have been dark at that time.

Once I was happy with the flat colours, I double checked that I had the correct colours for each character. (see Tiny Tims pants, Bobs scarf. Doh!) I then added the Moon for more effect. This also gave me my main light source and the panel graphics were complete.

I added Dave's text along with the scrolls and then my own dialogue. The song in this panel was written by me when I was 11 years old for a BBC TV Carol Contest on the programme 'Nationwide'.

I didn't win.